CW00656618

From Talking to Handwriting

Other titles in the **Key Strategies** series

Planning Primary Science by Roy Richardson, Phillip Coote and Alan Wood
Primary Science A Complete Reference Guide by Michael Evans
Physical Education A Practical Guide by Elizabeth Robertson
Helping with Handwriting by Rosemary Sassoon

Dedicated to the memory of my husband **Douglas M Tasker**

and our family without whose help and encouragement we

might never have completed *From Talking to Handwriting,*

and to acknowledge the help of many friends and colleagues,

especially Dr Beve Hornsby of the Hornsby International Centre,

London, for advice and research with regard to the Orton Papers;

Helen Eadington; Pauline Amos; Peter Dixon Design and Jillian Enright.

'This is it!'

DI.

'Train up a child in the way he should go:
and when he is old, he will not depart from it'.
(Proverbs C22 v6)

From Talking to Handwriting

Key Stages
1 & 2

Daphne M Tasker

John Murray

Illustrations by Christopher Mutter and Technical Art Services
Handwriting by John Townson/Creation
Cover Illustration by Tom Cross

© Daphne Tasker 1995

First published in 1995
by John Murray (Publishers) Ltd
50 Albemarle Street, London W1X 4BD

All rights reserved. This publication is copyright but permission is granted to teachers to make copies of
the following pages 15–19; 24–28; 30–61; 66–107; 111–126; and 128–150 by photocopying or other
duplicating processes, for use within their own school (or other educational institution). This permission
does not extend to the making of copies (e.g. in a resource centre) for use outside the institution in which
they are made, nor to the making of copies for hire or re-sale, nor to schools where the books are not used
as the main text.

Typeset by Litho Link Ltd., Welshpool, Powys, Wales in Rockwell and Sassoon
Layout by Christie Archer
Printed in Great Britain by St Edmundsbury Press Ltd, Bury St Edmunds

A CIP catalogue record for this book is available from the British Library

ISBN 0–7195–7134–0

■ Contents

Section 3 Handwriting Worksheets – Joining

Section 4 Perception and Patterning Worksheets

Section 5 Wallcharts

■ Preface

The handwriting scheme

This handwriting scheme is an empirical, teacher-led practical approach to the teaching of handwriting in the classroom. It is suitable for main-stream children and for less able children, working in groups or on a one-to-one basis. A step by step introduction to the scheme is given explaining the 'model' used to group the letters of the alphabet: a simple letter grouping upon which most of this scheme is based.

It is assumed that prior to working with this scheme children will have had the benefit of pre-writing experience using a variety of writing materials and instruments; scribbling, drawing, 'patterning', etc., at the pre-school stage and in the early years of Infant/Primary School.

Progressive learning

The concept of this scheme evolved from research and from discussions during a special class project with children on 'Letters of the alphabet', a topic initiated by the children themselves, who needed to revise the alphabet while improving their handwriting and reading skills. The project prompted some interesting questions which included:

- How did the children themselves perceive the shape and form of each individual letter?
- What concepts of size and shape did the children recognise?
- Could the children place the letters into matching 'family' groups or sets?
- Did the children realise that each letter had a shape, a sound and a name?

Lessons with the class were recorded over a long period and transcriptions of the recordings were used as a basis for the structure of the practical worksheets and for the formation of each letter and then each group of letters of the alphabet to be used in the classroom situation.

The title of the scheme *From Talking to Handwriting* explains the main concept and aim of the scheme. Speech and verbal reasoning play an important part in the learning process. The worksheets stress the importance of a phonetic approach. The learning progresses from the alphabet sounds to the letter names leading to the formation and structure of each letter.

In her book *Interpreting Handwriting* (1976) Jane Paterson writes:

> It is of little use to try to teach children to read and write before they have mastered the basic skills relating to space, judging distances, the control of hand movements, the remembering of simple sounds, the remembering of simple shapes and the co-ordination between all these and the eyes.

See it, say it, write it, read it

This is the working theme that flows throughout this book, which aims to give the child an understanding of all four skills by introducing a simple and workable scheme which is easily implemented and which forms the basis for well structured and clear handwriting. Success in handwriting is largely achieved by stressing the fact that each of the twenty-six letters of the alphabet is a recognisable shape and form and that groups of these letters are built up into individual words.

Background research

There can be little doubt that the standard of handwriting has steadily declined for many years and is now at a low ebb. A great deal of research and thought has gone into trying to find a remedy, and new theories are being propounded almost daily. There are many different opinions on how handwriting should be taught and it is very difficult for the teacher to select a logical and sequential approach to their teaching.

Previous research

The research carried out in the 1930s and the 1940s by Samuel T. Orton, and the works of Anna Gillingham and Bessie Stillman in the 1930s in connection with dyslexia, spelling and handwriting are as relevant now as they were then. This is also true of the research by Grace Fernald in 1943 into the multi-sensory system, VAKT (Visual, Auditory, Kinesthetic, Tactile) which stresses the 'whole word' approach to memory training. However, Gillingham and Stillman favour the simpler approach of tracing techniques to teach individual letters and the importance of phonics – sounds _ and the names of the alphabet letters (SOS _ Simultaneous Oral Spelling): see/hear/write, following the Orton theory.

Current research and the National Curriculum

Subsequently, in the 1970s this applied research was carried on by Janet Lerner in her book *Children with Learning Difficulties* (1971) and by Newell C. Kephart in his book *The Slow Learner in the Classroom* (1971) who further emphasised the theory, diagnosis and teaching strategy relating to the multi-sensory approach to reading, writing and language skills.

Despite the welcome given to the Bullock Report (1976) by the Committee of Enquiry into Reading and the use of English, handwriting continued to receive a low priority. However, with the introduction of the National Curriculum, and the implementation of *The Education Act* (1986) and *The Education Reform Act* (1988), the skill requirement for the teaching of handwriting once again became apparent. There has been a paucity of research in this area during the intervening years, but the National Curriculum attainment targets continue to support this concept.

■ Introduction

The reasoning

Clear handwriting is an essential skill in the art of communication.

The letters of the alphabet represent the sounds of speech thus, in word form, they represent written and spoken language. Through life we must identify ourselves with our signature and communicate with the written word. For example, when seeking employment handwriting can be a vital factor. It can make the difference between academic success or failure; a child with a writing problem may have a learning problem and when it comes to exams even a partially illiterate hand can cause failure when success was within reach.

> The ability to keep one idea in mind, to formulate the idea in words and appropriate syntactic patterns, to plan the correct graphic form for each letter and word, to correctly manipulate the writing instrument to produce the letter shapes, to integrate complex eye–hand relationships, to have sufficient visual motor memory – all these are required in the act of writing.
>
> *Lerner (1971)*

Regardless of the importance of modern technology – word processors, computers and electronic typewriters – handwriting can never be replaced. Despite living in an age of computer keyboards and 'book' computers with which handwritten data can be electronically recorded, handwriting is still an essential skill.

The scheme is not purely an academic exercise. It is the result of work carried out with children in classroom situations where problems have presented themselves with no apparent remedy to hand. It is a system that has been put to the test in the classroom and proved to be successful and, perhaps most important of all, it is a system which is easily understood and absorbed by child and teacher alike. The Plowden Report states:

> The motive for learning may arise from the children, or may be stimulated by discussion between teacher and children. The teacher can help the children to become aware of problems and to recognise the need for specific knowledge.
>
> *Central Advisory Council for Education (England) (1967)*

The method

Some children do not grasp the basics of handwriting and reading in the early days of their education and thus fall behind their contemporaries. This is largely because they have not, in many cases, been taught, or else have not fully understood, the basic primary skills of:

* Seeing – the shape of letters (visual).
* Hearing – the sounds of letters (auditory).
* Recognition – the recognition of letters (perceptual).
* Speaking – the vocalising of letters (oral).

One of the main difficulties facing teachers who have very limited teaching time is the need to teach handwriting to both children with normal ability and to those with special needs, which may lead to inconsistent approaches to the techniques of teaching the skills of handwriting.

Main-stream children and those with special needs require a teaching scheme which helps them with both letter formation and letter recognition, the one reinforcing the other.

The writing model

The writing model has a consistency of style for each letter of the alphabet being taught. It is a simple, structured method with as few rules and letter variations as possible thus making the learning process easier for the children.

There is no attempt to impose a rigidity of style. Children should be given the opportunity to pattern their own ideas of letter shape and form and should be encouraged to find words to talk about them; to 'verbalise' their ideas. Concept formation and language are closely related and it is necessary for the teacher to lead the child, partly by example and partly by definite guidance, to see relationships and classify shapes.

Understanding and the teaching of these skills will provide the means of acquiring a basic 'hand' which can be modified and adapted later to a child's individual requirements and characteristics so that a personal writing style will evolve. Like fingerprints, all handwriting differs with the individual. Once the child has mastered the essential mechanics of handwriting, individual characteristics may be safely encouraged.
Handwritten sheets are seldom print 'perfect'. The handwriting model used in this book is as consistent and accurate as possible.

In *Handwriting Review* (1990) Rosemary Sassoon reviewed Dom Patrick Barry's *Handwriting Sheets* which were first produced in 1952. She observed:

> Dom Patrick's own words echo his common-sense, practical approach to handwriting: 'The writing of these sheets has been rather carefully done to serve as a model, but ordinary handwriting should be rapid and individual and never faultless.'

Handwriting – a whole school policy

Everyone has their own style of handwriting and teachers are no exception. The important factor is that all the basic training should be consistent.
The headteacher of a Middle School considered that handwriting and the presentation of work was the responsibility of all members of staff and advocated a whole school policy regarding handwriting covering all subjects of the Curriculum. A memorandum circulated to all the staff at the school stated:

1. The first aim must be for every teacher, in every lesson and in every subject, to raise the level of what is acceptable presentation. 'Sloppy' work should be rejected and repeated, preferably in the pupil's own time. Pupils must be quickly made aware that there is no multiplicity of standards available anywhere in the school.
2. Incidentally, does your own board work set a good example? A teacher's handwriting should set a good example for children to follow with particular emphasis being placed on the care and the legibility of Assignments and Worksheets which children have to read and understand.
3. There are many unfair criticisms levelled against schools and teachers, but one which is very difficult to answer is that children write badly, spell badly and present work badly. I think that at this moment we must plead guilty – and do something about it.

Handwriting – the objective

In the midst of all the theory and instruction the paramount point to remember is the ultimate objective; the quality of life of the pupil, whether child or adult. No matter how effective a programme may be, it is of no avail without the co-operation of the pupil and, in the main, this can only be gained by constant and unremitting encouragement. The pupil must be persuaded to realise that he or she *can* learn as well as anyone else and it is hoped that this book will enable the teacher to help the pupil to fulfil this aspiration.

From Talking to Handwriting is a scheme that can be applied with equal success to both younger and older children and it also has an application for those who suffer from dyslexia (disturbance of reading), dysgraphia (disturbance of writing), and aphasia (disturbance of speech).
Teaching a pupil to write with this structured scheme can be a rewarding experience for the teacher and, of more importance, a source of immense pleasure, pride and sense of achievement for the pupil.

The use of lined paper

Whatever the policy adopted in the early stages of education, children ultimately have to write on lines. They have to deal with lined paper in work books and loose-leaf sheets and, later in life, will have to cope with many matters on lined paper. The earlier they master this particular skill the easier it will be for them to fully master the complex skills of handwriting. However, up to the age of about six years, plain paper is generally recommended in schools for scribbling, making patterns and forms leading to the writing of letters of the alphabet.

The second stage is usually that of the written word, and it is here that the child can have his or her first experience of writing on lines. General policy is that the teacher draws a single base line near the child's drawing upon which to write the child's name, a text or title. This provides a guideline for the letters to sit on as in Figure 1.

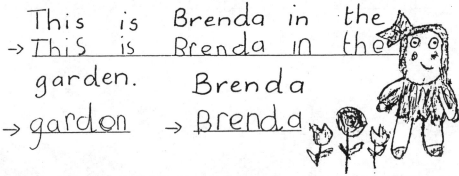

Figure 1: A guideline for the letters to sit on (Age 5 years, 6 months).

Care should be taken at this stage to have only one line or the child might try to write between the lines instead of using each line as a base line. The results may then appear as in Figure 2.

Figure 2: Writing *between* the lines (Age 5 years).

A line above the writing can cause problems for children who find it difficult to perceive the differences between letter heights and the relative proportions of tall and small letters. Figure 3 shows the writing of a child who is unsure of the relative proportions of tall and small letters.

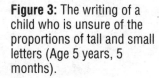

Figure 3: The writing of a child who is unsure of the proportions of tall and small letters (Age 5 years, 5 months).

Once a child's handwriting indicates that perceptual and motor development are mature, as indicated through performances such as that shown in Figure 3, lined paper can be fully utilised. Lines provide an invaluable guide to determining where an individual letter stands on the base line and enables the teacher to show how each letter should start in relation to the general pattern and formation. It enables the child to see that the ascending/tall letters start at or go up towards the line while descenders/tail letters start mid-way between the two lines and continue below the base line. It is in this aspect of teaching that the use of lined paper with a faint mid-line between two pairs of lines (Figure 4) will provide helpful guidance to the child.

Figure 4: Lined paper with a faint mid-line between each pair of lines.

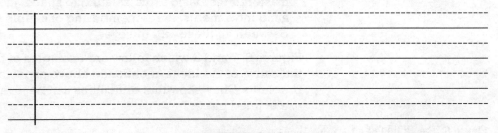

In the early stages of teaching children to use lined paper, it will help to teach them to use only alternate lines for writing (Figure 5). This policy will prevent letters from becoming joined up vertically, and also provide space between the lines for the teacher to make corrections – apart from which it makes the writing very much easier to read for both child and teacher.

Figure 5: Writing on alternate lines.

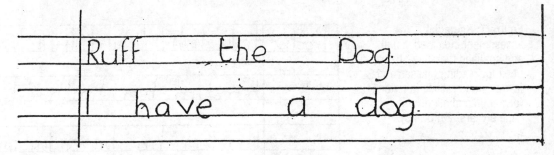

Perhaps most important of all, lined paper enables the teacher to make clear to the child the most important basic concepts such as top, bottom, tall, small, above, below, centre, middle, half-way, between, straight, curve, round etc., without which the child cannot hope to appreciate the visual impression and actual formation of letters.

There are several variations of paper design available. The types most commonly used in schools are plain paper and lined paper with the lines about 8 mm apart, covering the whole page except for the horizontal plain heading at the top and bottom, with a vertical margin on the left-hand side. Paper with a margin is not always necessary but it does give guidance and makes for neatness of presentation.

Paper is available with widely spaced lines, some have 'tramlines' while some have lines in groups of three or even four parallel lines. These are useful should a teacher require a specific style of paper layout for use with individual children with special needs.

Research has shown that a great deal can be achieved by thorough training of a child's perceptual ability (Orton, 1937; Fernald, 1943; Frostig and Horne, 1964). Any methods that can help a child to detect differences or similarities between patterns, shapes and forms of various kinds will bring the child nearer to being able to visually judge and appreciate what these differences are; a process which will, in due course, become automatic. It is at this stage, usually at the age of six or seven years, that lined paper becomes really useful to the child.

In her book *Interpreting Handwriting* Jane Paterson refers to the writing of Marty Stewart, an analyst who has made a special study of children's handwriting. She quotes as follows:

> If a normal bright and happy child is using the available space on the paper in a bizarre way which indicates that he has little or no idea of 'top', 'bottom', 'right' or 'left', he may well have a perceptual difficulty which should be investigated and helped at an early stage.

Paterson goes on to say:

> It is of little use to try to teach children to read and write before they have mastered the basic skills relating to space, judging distance, the control of hand movements, the remembering of simple shapes and the co-ordination between all these and the eyes.

Figures 6, 7 and 8 which follow are examples of the work of one child and are indicative of the ideas mentioned above especially in relation to visual problems. They show that difficulties can be overcome, especially with the use of lined paper.

Figure 6: The writing of an older child who is unsure of the proportions of tall and small letters in relation to writing on lined paper (Age 9 years).

Figure 7: Remedial assessment indicated visual and spatial difficulties, the need for reading glasses and for revision practice in letter formation and alignment (Age 9 years, 2 months).

Figure 8: Illustrates the progress and improvement after remedial measures were initiated – compare with Figure 6 (Age 9 years, 4 months).

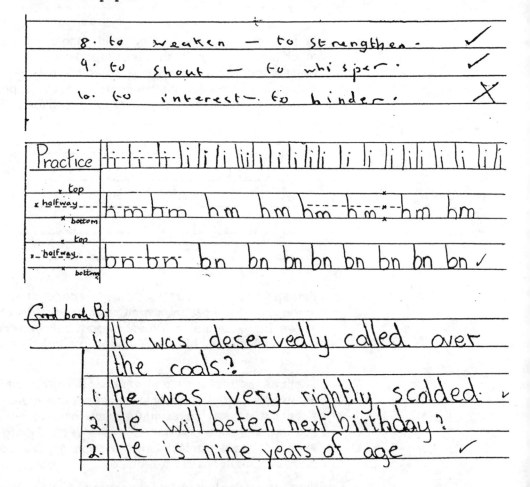

The use of lined paper can make a great contribution to the teaching of spacial concepts. Perhaps it is appropriate that the final word on this matter should be from the report *Writing Lines – an Exploratory Study* (1975), in which Burnhill *et al.,* who conducted research comparing children's handwriting on lined and unlined paper in three Staffordshire schools, stated:

> Research in British primary schools in 1974 showed that children of six and seven years improved the legibility of their writing and overall structure of work when lined paper was used. Teachers who previously provided unlined paper were so impressed with the children's improved work that they changed their policy.

1
Assessment

■ Individual assessment

The use of the word 'Assessment' refers to formal assessment or testing which confirms a teacher's own classroom observations.

> The first problem is to identify the point of breakdown. When this point has been discovered training techniques can be applied which will help the child in overcoming his difficulty and aid his development. The teacher needs to observe the performance of the child which will indicate the need or level of development. The teacher is then able to evaluate the child's ability and performance.
>
> *The Slow Learner in the Classroom, Newell C. Kephart*

It is most important at the outset to establish the stage of a child's development and progress at school with regard to infant and older children. Individual assessment is required to identify underlying problems, and to determine any defects in handwriting. It is also useful with some children to gauge their standard of reading in order to assess reading age and ability in relation to their chronological age, their peer group in class, and performance against the requirements of the National Curriculum.

The majority of schools, and Local Authorities, use Standardised Reading Tests to establish an individual reading age and standard Score/Normal Reference Tests. Catalogues can be obtained from publishing houses which specialise in Assessment Test Materials (listed on page 9).

In the following pages methods of evaluation are shown which have been devised to enable the teacher to assess the basic problems confronting a child when being taught to write.
These evaluations cover:

1. Left- or right-handed
2. Posture and hand hold
3. Motor control and co-ordination
4. Letter shape
5. Names and sounds of letters
6. Left to right co-ordination and eye control
7. Spacing of words and alignment
8. Perception
9. Visual and auditory memory retention – listening.

Considering these aspects when assessing the performance of a child, an individual revision programme to cater for the child's requirements can be devised and put into practice.

In the assessments, the alphabet has been divided into **five specific letter groups** which form the basis of this scheme. We cannot re-invent the alphabet which has served us for over 2000 years, but we can re-arrange it into groups for easy recognition, thus aiding the acquisition of reading and writing skills.
The aim for children with poor handwriting is to make the revision of skills as easy as possible and to enable the child to produce handwriting which is fluently written and easily read. A careful appraisal of the child's ability and potential, particularly in the context of the developmental age of the child, is an important factor when considering the correction of the child's work. An analysis of current work is important and it is helpful to have samples from other curricula subjects.

Letter formation
Defects in writing are due largely to faulty manipulation of the writing instrument and an inadequate knowledge of letter shapes and structure.

A child finds it difficult to copy shapes unless he knows *how* to do so. Knowing what to do is still only a part of the answer – fingers have to be trained to do it. Recognition and the copying of shapes is not enough;

understanding the way in which letters should be formed is essential. Memory and recall also play a very important role in learning skills.

Children need to be taught how to improve their writing and revision methods should be carefully explained. Telling the writer to 'do better', 'practise your letters', 'do this again'- all without specific instruction – is not helpful to a child and will in no way help to solve the problems.

Inconsistencies and letter formation mistakes are more clearly seen in a complete sentence. Therefore specific corrections of errors and practice exercises, properly explained and written down, are very valuable.

On completion of any work, letter formation errors, incorrect presentation, spacing, lack of correct technique and shortcomings should be identified and the child shown methods of correction. Children with untidy, poor handwriting are only too well aware of the fact and are eager to discuss their problem with a sympathetic listener. In this way children are made aware of their faults and inconsistencies which, with explanation and extra practice *can* be remedied. The recognition and overcoming of these limitations gives the child a sense of real achievement. Children often have to write out spelling mistakes several times for correction at the completion of an exercise. This can also apply to handwriting defects.

Consistent approach

An inadequate and inconsistent approach to teaching handwriting in Primary Schools can lead to many children having problems in middle and later schooling. It is of great advantage for children to be given a consistent approach to handwriting as they move from class to class, and from teacher to teacher, throughout the school especially in the earlier years. It is difficult for children if they are taught differing handwriting styles or methods at different stages as they progress through school.

There are many schemes on the market and many methods of assessment which are very valuable tools for the teacher. Nevertheless, a child's own assessment of his or her lack of good handwriting and the subsequent improvement is very uplifting for their morale. Their own work, as seen by the child, is factual and looking through their own books and files they can see proof of their own progress and attainments and this is even more helpful when filed assessments are maintained by the teacher.

Accurate assessment of a child's needs is of great importance. Without an accurate diagnosis, no remedy can be successful.

Methods of assessment

For the teacher
- Assessment – areas of further observation: a guide list (p.10)
- Posture, paper position and right- or left-handed (p.11)
- Letter formation assessments (pp.12–13)
- Guide list for each letter of the alphabet (pp.24–28)

For the child
- Test sheets 1 to 4 – to assess a child's ability and level of performance. To be administered and observed by the teacher. These sheets may be photocopied and retained as a record of progress.

Assessment materials

Assessment materials can be obtained from:
NFER Nelson , 2 Oxford Road East, Windsor, Berkshire SL4 1DF
Hodder and Stoughton, 338 Euston Road, London NW1 3BH

■ Areas of further observation: a guide list

1 All observations should be made on a one-to-one basis except a written piece of prose.
2 The page references refer to extra sheets which may be used in assessment.
  Some of these sheets may form the basis of a wall display.

Observe and test	Observation and remedial action
Right- or left-handed and position (observe)	Right-handed children should place the paper to the right of the centre line of the body. Left-handed children should place the paper to the left of the centre line of the body. Observe that the paper is positioned to allow hand and forearm to rest upon the table (p.11).
Posture and hand hold	If the child is not sitting comfortably or is gripping the pencil too tightly, pressing very hard or is very tense, he will have difficulty in achieving good writing skills. Watch the child while he is writing (pp.15 and 17).
Motor control and co-ordination (observe)	Important to note consistency of size, spacing, orientation, alignment and fine motor control.
Letter shape (directionality) (observe)	Observe child forming each letter to note start and ending positions and to check that each letter can be written in sequential order and in the group forms (pp. 31–61).
Name and sound of each letter (Tests 3 and 4)	Is there any evidence of a hearing impairment? Child's hearing to be checked if any difficulty is experienced – audiologist.
Left to right co-ordination and eye control (observe or Tests 2–4)	Observe child's eye movements. Lack of ocular control should be further tested by optician.
Spacing of words and alignment (Test 1)	Does the child understand the grouping of the letters to form words and maintain alignment of the letters? Can the child write a structured, sequenced piece of prose?
Perceptual assessment	Perceptual and patterning evaluation exercises (pp. 111–126).

■ Posture, paper position and right- or left-handed

1. Right-handed child

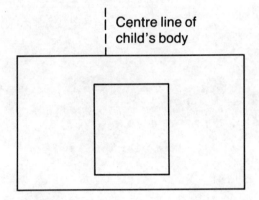

3. Left-handed child

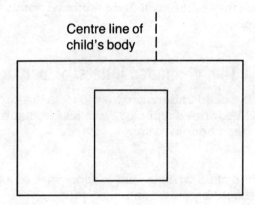

2. Right-handed child

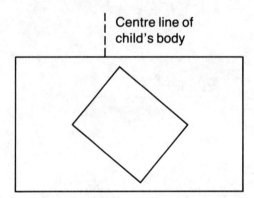

4. Left-handed child

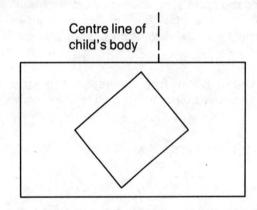

Right-handed children should place the paper to the right of the central line of the body. Left-handed children should place the paper to the left of the central line of the body.
Observe that the paper is positioned to allow the hand and the forearm to rest upon the table.

■ Letter formation assessments

The following are examples of checking for inconsistencies in a child's handwriting. This list is by no means inexhaustible and doubtless the teacher will find additional points through experience.

Group 1 The 'c'-shaped letters: c o a u e s

- Does the child understand how to form the curve in 'c'? It should be formed anti-clockwise and from top to bottom rather than bottom to top.

- Does the child write 'o' and 'c' clockwise or anti-clockwise? Both should be drawn anti-clockwise.

- Does the child's 'u' have a down stroke or 'stand', or is it simply a 'u' shape? A stand facilitates an exit point for joining purposes. It also avoids confusion with the letter 'v'.

- Does the 'e' start from the base of the letter in a reverse stroke up and curve clockwise? It should be drawn anti-clockwise.

- Does 's' start from the bottom or the top of the letter? It should start from the top of the letter.

- Observe the child's ability to write on a straight line to avoid 'floating' letters.

Group 2 The 'm'-shaped letters: i r n m

- Does the child start the letters from the bottom and go up to the top missing out the down stoke? These letters should be written from the top to the bottom.

Group 3 The tall letters – ascenders: l h b k f t d

- Does the child form ascending letters to an even height or is there some confusion between small and tall letters? For instance does the 'h' look like an 'n', or a 'd' like an 'a'?

- At times a child forms ascending letters from the base line. All ascenders other than 'd' start from the top of the letter and stand on the base line.

- Can the child differentiate between 'b' and 'd'? To help 'b'/'d' reversal difficulties – say 'h' into 'b', 'c' into 'd'.

- Does the child form 'b' like the number 6 or reversed or without a stand? Letter 'b' starts with an 'l' shape, returns halfway and curves over to the base line. For reversal difficulties – say 'h' into 'b'.

- Does the child form letter 'd' from the top? This is wrong. Letter 'd' should start as a 'c' shape and continue up from the base line to the top line and return down to the base line. For reversal difficulties – say 'c' into 'd'.

- Letter 'k'. Does the child draw the < of the letter 'k' in proportion?

- Letter 'f'. Does the child form the letter 'f' correctly from the top of the letter to the base line or the reverse which is incorrect?

  For joined writing use this form.

- Controversial 't'. Letter 't' formed thus 't'can be confused with a plus sign. Letter 't' formed thus 't' can lead to an exaggerated elongated stroke. This form of 't' is a more simple shape.

  In joined handwriting 't' should be joined from the base line, not from the stroke.

Group 4 The tail letters – descenders: *j y g qu p*

- Does the child form the whole letter above the line? The body of the letter should be on the base line.

- Does the child form the letter incorrectly from the tail upwards? Tail letters or descenders should be formed from the top of the letter to the bottom.

- Children find it easier to allow 'q' to flow into the 'u', which seems logical from the child's point of view as they have learned that 'q' phonetically sounds as 'q' (qu) (kw) (*Note:* 'q' in spelling - all words containing 'q' have 'u' following.)

Group 5 The 'v'-shaped letters: *v w x z*

- Occasionally a child will form the 'v' shaped letters from right to left – this is incorrect. These letters should be formed from left to right.

■ Assessment test sheets 1–4

Test sheet 1

Write a story about yourself and your family, your friends, your hobbies and the things you like doing (p.15)

Test sheet 2

Can you say each letter of the alphabet? Write down all the letters of the alphabet on to these lines (p.17).

Test sheet 3

Do you know the names and sounds of the letters of the alphabet (p.18)?

Test sheet 4

Do you know the names and sounds of the letters of the alphabet in these five groups (p.19)?

Test sheet 1

Name _____   Date _____ Age _____

_____   **Left-/right-handed**

Write a story about yourself and your family, your friends, your hobbies
and the things you like doing.

Test sheet 1

Name _____   Date _____   Age _____

_____   Left-/right-handed

_____

_____

_____

_____

_____

_____

_____

_____

_____

_____

_____

_____

_____

_____

_____

_____

_____

_____

_____

_____

_____

Areas of revision practice: **Teacher's observation:**

                              © JOHN MURRAY   FROM TALKING TO HANDWRITING

Test sheet 2

Name _____

Date _____ Age _____

Left-/right-handed _____

Can you say each letter of the alphabet?

1.   c   o   a   u   e   s

2.   i   r   n   m

3.   l   h   b   k   f   t   d

4.   j   y   g   qu   p

5.   v   w   x   z

Copy each letter of the alphabet on to these lines.

Your teacher will watch you write each letter.

1.	
2.	
3.	
4.	
5.	

Areas of revision practice: **Teachers' observation:**

Test sheet 3

Name _____   Date _____ Age _____

_____   Left-/right-handed _____

Do you know the names and sounds of the letters of the alphabet?

	a	b	c	d	e	f	g
name	___	___	___	___	___	___	___
sound	___	___	___	___	___	___	___

	h	i	j	k	l	m	n
name	___	___	___	___	___	___	___
sound	___	___	___	___	___	___	___

	o	p	qu	r	s	t	u
name	___	___	___	___	___	___	___
sound	___	___	___	___	___	___	___

	v	w	x	y	z
name	___	___	___	___	___
sound	___	___	___	___	___

Your teacher will tick the letters as you say the name and sound for each letter.

Revision practice – letters to learn: **Teacher's observation:**

Test sheet 4

Name _____   Date _____ Age _____

_____   Left-/right-handed _____

Do you know the names and sounds of the letters of the alphabet in these five groups?

1.   c   o   a   u   e   s

name   ___   ___   ___   ___   ___   ___

sound   ___   ___   ___   ___   ___   ___

2.   i   r   n   m

name   ___   ___   ___   ___

sound   ___   ___   ___   ___

3.   l   h   b   k   f   t   d

name   ___   ___   ___   ___   ___   ___   ___

sound   ___   ___   ___   ___   ___   ___   ___

4.   j   y   g   qu   p

name   ___   ___   ___   ___   ___

sound   ___   ___   ___   ___   ___

5.   v   w   x   z

name   ___   ___   ___   ___

sound   ___   ___   ___   ___

Your teacher will tick the letters as you say each letter name and sound.

Letter formation practice: **Teacher's observation:**

© JOHN MURRAY   FROM TALKING TO HANDWRITING

2
Handwriting Worksheets – Printing

■ Method and instructions

Handwriting is a physical activity; a fine motor development which develops in a different way for each individual. Writing is a special language, it is a key to learning.

Children need to understand the process of handwriting, they need to be helped to see how the process works.

Alphabet sheets

The alphabet sheet, entitled 'Sounds of the letters with key pictures' (p.24) is the sequence followed throughout the scheme. Each letter is linked with a corresponding picture illustrating the shape and form of each individual letter which, in turn, represents the shape and formation of the first letter of each printed word, for example:

Name	Graphic picture	Sound	Word
'<u>a</u>'		/a/	<u>a</u>pple
'<u>b</u>'		/b/	<u>b</u>anana
'<u>c</u>'		/k/	<u>c</u>at

This format is repeated throughout the worksheets – a consistent approach in the development of visual recognition, memory and recall, in order to help the child to develop these very important aspects in the process of early learning skills.

Worksheets

There are two types of worksheets. Some contain instructions which are written primarily for the teacher who is helping the child to acquire the skills of handwriting. Older children may be able to read these sheets for themselves depending upon their individual reading and writing skills. For this reason they have been produced using a juvenile typeface. The teacher will have to use his or her knowledge of the standard and ability of the child or children concerned.

The first few sheets give an explanation of how the letters are formed and why they are grouped as they are. There is also a list of practice words from letter groups 1 and 2.

The second group of worksheets is aimed specifically at the pupils. The exercises should be explained to the children before they copy the worksheets, the teacher choosing the appropriate page and reading the instructions through with the child or children explaining how to follow and copy the written letters and words.

The first part of the pupil's worksheets gives instruction.

The concepts of shape, size, top, bottom, middle etc., are discussed.

The formation of each letter may be illustrated on the board or on paper while explaining verbally the name and phonic sound of each letter, how it is formed and written down.

To recognise and 'see' the shape and form of an individual letter, verbally acknowledging it by sound (phonetic) and then copying the shape reinforces the learning skill which gives meaning to the activity.

These worksheets have also been produced using a juvenile typeface as children have been found to relate more easily to this style of written word. The pages are also similar to pages in school exercise books and, more importantly, the writing is easily read and understood by the child.

The letter shapes, size, formation and the setting out of the work on lined

paper familiar to the child mean far more than printed instructions on an

otherwise blank piece of paper. The handwritten worksheets are recognised as 'handwriting'. As children are able to read the sheets more easily this facilitates the reading process.

The worksheets can be used by the teacher to demonstrate and to talk to a group of children or on a one-to-one basis about each letter of the alphabet and to discuss the letter formation, sound and letter name of the letters of the alphabet.

The system stresses the need to reinforce all the sensory aspects; the child needs to:

LOOK, SAY/SOUND, WRITE and READ throughout the scheme.

The format follows the grouping of the letters illustrated in the text.

The goal of handwriting instruction is to help the child to develop a useful communication tool. The child should develop a skill in writing legibly and be able to accomplish writing with ease.

J.M. Lerner

■ Sounds of the letters with key pictures

Name		Sound	Name		Sound
'a'		/a/ apple	'n'		/n/ nail
'b'		/b/ banana	'o'		/o/ orange
'c'		/k/ cat	'p'		/p/ pipe
'd'		/d/ drum	'q' (qu)		/kw/ queen
'e'		/e/ elephant	'r'		/r/ rope
'f'		/f/ fish	's'		/s//z/ snake
'g'		/g/ girl	't'		/t/ teddy
'h'		/h/ horse	'u'		/u/umbrella
'i'		/i/ indian	'v'		/v/ vase
'j'		/j/ jug	'w'		/w/ worm
'k'		/k/key	'x'		/ks//gz/box
'l'/		l/ lamp	'y'		/y/ yoyo
'm'		/m/ monster	'z'		/z/ zip

© JOHN MURRAY   FROM TALKING TO HANDWRITING

■ The letters of the alphabet

Here are the letters of the alphabet.

a b c d e f g h i j k l m

n o p q r s t u v w x y z

Words are made up of these letters.

<u>Each letter has:</u>

<u>a letter sound</u>

<u>a letter name</u>

<u>a letter shape.</u>

How many letters are there in the alphabet?

There are twenty-six (26) letters in the alphabet.

We have talked about all the letters of the alphabet.

We have said the <u>names</u> of each letter.

We have said the <u>sounds</u> of each letter.

We found out that if we put all the letters into different groups and patterns, this helped us to see and remember the shape and the sound of the letters more easily when we had to write them down. Some of the <u>letters of the alphabet</u> are easy to write. Some letters are hard to draw. There are <u>small halfway letters</u>. There are <u>tall letters</u>. There are <u>tail letters</u> which sit on a line, the tail is written under the line. The letters have different shapes. It is easier to learn to draw or write the letters of the alphabet if they are put into <u>groups of the same shape</u>. It is helpful to write on lined paper.

© JOHN MURRAY   FROM TALKING TO HANDWRITING

■ Alphabet letter groups

To help us with alphabet letter names and letter sounds we sorted the letters into groups of letters which help to form a different letter.

Group 1   c o a u e s   **c letter shapes**

C   helps to make c O

O   helps to make a a

C   shape is part of u u

C   shape is also part of e e e

S   has two (2) C shapes S s S   c o a u e s

Group 2   i r n m   **m letter shapes**

i/i   shape helps to make r r

r   shape helps to make n n

n   shape helps to make m m   i r n m

Group 3   l h b k f t d   **Tall letters – ascenders**

l   helps to make h h

h/h helps to make b b   (for reversal problems say 'h'
                              into 'b'.)
      l/k f t

C helps to make d d   (for reversal problems say 'c' into 'd'.)

l h b k f t d

© JOHN MURRAY   FROM TALKING TO HANDWRITING

Group 4   *j y g qu p*   **Tail letters – descenders**

i/i   helps to make   ¡ j

u/u   helps to make   ụ y

a/a   helps to make   g̣ g

q   helps to make   qu̇   qu

qu   join together as a letter sound

        to help spelling

pn   makes a practice pattern   ᴦ ᴘ p

        (down, up and round.)

                                    j y g qu p

Group 5   v w x z v   *v* **letter shapes**

V   is part of V̇V̇ W

X   has 4 'v' shapes ※ X

Z   has 2 'v' shapes Z̄ Z

                                    V W X Z

          © JOHN MURRAY   FROM TALKING TO HANDWRITING

■ Printing skills

Using the worksheets

Each worksheet explains:

1. The start point. The name and phonetic sound of each letter.
2. How the letter is formed: shape, size.
3. Verbal instructions in order to form each letter.
4. Practice patterns to reinforce the letter formation.
5. The child is asked to give the name and sound of each letter and to demonstrate the shape, for example, 'The letter 'a' says /a/ and is shaped like this...'. The letter is then written.
6. There is space at the bottom of each worksheet for the practice of individual letters.

Word building

1. The early introduction of the teaching of handwriting with word building and spelling is as important. Phonics – sounds, and the formation of letter shapes and the building of words, go hand in hand with conceptual and motor activities.
2. Alphabet letter groups 1 and 2 cover all the vowels, therefore the child is in a position to practice handwriting and word building skills.

Lists of useful words made up from letter groups 1 and 2 are given on page p.30. The teacher will be able to collate further lists as the remainder of the alphabet is learned.

Group 1   *letter 'c' shapes*   c o a u e s
Group 2   *letter 'm' shapes*   i r n m

Children can be encouraged to make words using the letters that they have learned during the handwriting sessions.

■ Practice words from letter groups 1 and 2

Group 1 c o a u e s

Two letters	Three letters	Four letters	Five letters
as	ace	ease	cause
us	ass	sees	cease
so	cue		cocoa
	sea		sauce
	see		
	sue		
	use		

Group 2 i r n m

Two letters	Three letters
in	rim

Combination of group 1 letters (c o a u e s) and group 2 letters (i r n m)

Two letters	Three letters		Four letters		Five letters	Six letters
am	ace	sir	cane	nine	acorn	murmur
an	aim	son	care	nose	cause	rescue
as	arc	sue	coin	race	cease	scream
in	arm	sum	come	rain	cocoa	summer
me	ass	use	cone	ear	cream	
on	can	sun	core	rein	means	
or	car	are	corn	rice	miner	
so	cue		earn	rise	mince	
us	ear		ease	roam	mouse	
is	ice		home	roar	sauce	
	man		hose	room	scare	
	men		iron	rose	scone	
	mum		mane	same	score	
	oar		main	sane	siren	
	one		mean	scar	snore	
	our		mice	seam		
	ram		mine	seem		
	ran		moan	seen		
	roe		moon	sees		
	rum		more	some		
	sea		name	soon		
	see		near	sore		
			nice			

© JOHN MURRAY   FROM TALKING TO HANDWRITING

Letter 'c' shapes
Group 1
Print

 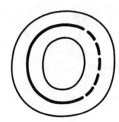 

c   o   a

u   e   s

© JOHN MURRAY   FROM TALKING TO HANDWRITING

C

 cat

c is a small halfway letter c ===== top
===== halfway
bottom

<u>Say and write</u> c curve c c

<u>Copy the picture of</u>

<u>the cat</u>

<u>Practice patterns</u>

c curve c   c c c   c c c   c c c   c c c

c c c c

c c c   c c c

Small halfway c   Tall (capital) C Cc Cc

c c

C c C

© JOHN MURRAY   FROM TALKING TO HANDWRITING

o orange

o is a small halfway letter o ⎯⎯ top
                               ⎯⎯ halfway
                                  bottom

<u>Say and write</u> c into o. c c o o

Copy the picture of

the orange

<u>Practice patterns</u>

cc co co co coo coo

c o

coo

Small halfway o   Tall (capital) OOoOo

oo oo

OoO

a

apple

a is a small halfway letter a ⎯⎯⎯ top
halfway
bottom

<u>Say and write</u> c into c into a a

<u>Copy the picture of</u>

the apple

<u>Practice patterns</u>

coa coa aaa aaa

co

oa

Small halfway a   Tall (capital)A A a A a

a a

AaA

© JOHN MURRAY   FROM TALKING TO HANDWRITING

u  umbrella

u is a small halfway letter u ⎯⎯ top
⎯⎯ halfway
bottom

A c curve helps to make a ∪ shape

<u>Say and write</u>　∪ curve and stand ∪ ∪

<u>Copy the picture of</u>

<u>the umbrellas</u>

<u>Practice patterns</u>

∪　curve and stand ∪ ∪ ∪

∪ ∪ ∪　∪ ∪　∪ ∪

c u　c u

a u　a u

Small halfway u　　Tall (capital) U Uu Uu

u u u

U u U

e  elephant

e is a small halfway e ------- top
====== halfway
bottom

<u>Say and write</u> Draw a short line ⇒
and add a letter c curve ⇐ ⟨e⟩ e

<u>Copy the picture of</u>

<u>the elephant</u>

<u>Practice patterns</u>

−ce −ce ece ece

ec ec

coe

cee cee

Small halfway e   Tall (capital) E E e E e

ee

E e E

© JOHN MURRAY   FROM TALKING TO HANDWRITING

s  snake

s is a small halfway letter s ----- top
----- halfway
----- bottom

<u>Say and write</u> Small ͼc and small
backwards ͽ go together to make § ş s

Copy the picture of

the snake

<u>Practice patterns and words</u>

§ş   §ş   §ş   §ş   §ş   §ş

as

us

see

Small halfway s   Tall (capital) S S s S s

s s s

S s S

Letter 'm' shapes
Group 2
Print

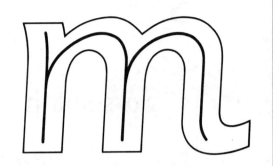

i

r

n

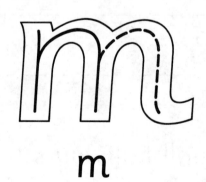

m

© JOHN MURRAY   FROM TALKING TO HANDWRITING

i

 indian

i is a small halfway letter i ----- top
----- halfway
----- bottom

Start halfway between the top and bottom
line ----- *halfway* draw a line down *× i↓ i*

Say and write Short line and dot i i i

Copy the picture of

the indian

Practice patterns and words

ii ii iii iiii

is

sea

see

Small halfway i   Tall (capital)I I I

i i i

|i

r

rope

r is a small halfway letter r ----- top
----- halfway
----- bottom

<u>Say and write</u> Letter i changes into i i r r

<u>Copy the picture of</u>

<u>the rope</u>

<u>Practice patterns and words</u>

i i r r   i r r   r r r   r r r

or

car

are

Small halfway r   Tall (capital) R R r R r

r r

R r R

© JOHN MURRAY   FROM TALKING TO HANDWRITING

n  nail

n is a small halfway letter n ‒‒‒‒‒ top
‒‒‒‒‒ halfway
‒‒‒‒‒ bottom

<u>Say and write</u> Letter i changes into i͏r͏ r,
letter r changes into n ii rn irn

Copy the picture of

the nails

<u>Practice patterns and words</u>

irn   irn   n n   n n n

an

can

s u n

Small halfway n   Tall (capital) N Nn Nn

n n

NnN

m  monster

m is a small halfway letter m ----- top
halfway
bottom

<u>Say and write</u> Letter i changes into irr,
r changes into n, n changes into mirnm

<u>Copy the picture of</u>

<u>the monster</u>

<u>Practice patterns and words</u>

irnm   irnm   irnm   mm

am

men

sum

Small halfway m   Tall (capital) M Mm Mm

mm

MmM

© JOHN MURRAY   FROM TALKING TO HANDWRITING

Tall letters
Group 3
Print Ascenders

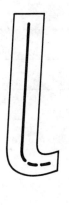
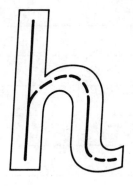
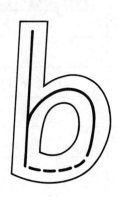

l   h   b

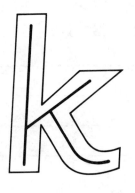

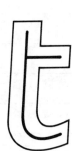

k   f   t   d

© JOHN MURRAY FROM TALKING TO HANDWRITING

_l_

lamp

l is a tall letter l — top / halfway / bottom   l l l l

Letter i and letter l make a practice pattern.

<u>Say and write</u> i changes into l i l

Practice patterns and words

il   il   il   il   lll

all

call

sell

Tall letter l   Tall (capital) L L l L l

l l l

L l L

© JOHN MURRAY   FROM TALKING TO HANDWRITING

h

horse

h is a tall letter h ⎯ top
⎯ halfway
⎯ bottom   h h h h

Letter | and letter h make a practice pattern.

<u>Say and write</u> | changes into h h

<u>Practice patterns and words</u>

lh lh lh hh

him

her

has

Tall letter h   Tall (capital) H H h H h

h h

H h H

b  banana

b is a tall letter b ⎯ top / halfway / bottom   b b b b

Letter h and letter b make a practice pattern

<u>Say and write</u> h changes into h/b b

Practice patterns and words

hb   hb   bb   bb

be

bus

rub

Tall letter b   Tall (capital) B b B b

bb

BbB

   © JOHN MURRAY   FROM TALKING TO HANDWRITING

k

 key

k is a tall letter k ═══ top / halfway / bottom   k k k k

Letter | and a < (vee) shape make a practice pattern

<u>Say and write</u> | add a < shape k k k

Practice patterns and words

k< k< kk kk

ink

ask

kiss

Tall letter k   Tall (capital) K K k K k

kk

KkK

f

 fish

Letter f is a tall letter f ‾‾ top ‾‾ halfway ‾‾ bottom   f f f f

An ↓f shape and a short line ⇢ make a practice pattern.

<u>Say and write</u>   ↓f shape add a short line ⇢• ⇢ff

Practice patterns and words

ff‾ ff‾ ff ff

fan

for

fill

Tall letter f   Tall (capital)F F f F f

ff

F ff

© JOHN MURRAY   FROM TALKING TO HANDWRITING

t

 *teddy*

Letter t is a tall letter t ----- top, halfway, bottom   t t t t

An l shape and a short line t make a practice pattern.

<u>Say and write</u> l shape add a short line t l t

<u>Practice patterns and words</u>

t⁻ t⁻ t⁻ tt ttt tt

at

lot   .

tell

Tall letter t   Tall (capital)T T t T t

tt

TtT

d

 drum

d is a tall letter d ≡ top / halfway / bottom d d d d

Letter c and letter d make a practice pattern.

<u>Say and write</u> c changes into c d

Practice patterns and words

c d   c d   c d d   c d d

and

did

bed

Tall letter d   Tall (capital)D D d D d

d d

D d D

© JOHN MURRAY   FROM TALKING TO HANDWRITING

Tail letters
Group 4 Descenders
Print

j

y

g

qu

p

© JOHN MURRAY   FROM TALKING TO HANDWRITING

j

j jug

j is a tail letter j —— top
—— halfway
—— bottom   j j j j

Letter i and letter j make a practice pattern.

<u>Say and write</u> i changes into i j j

Practice patterns and words

i i j   i i j   i j j   i j j

jar

jam

job

Tail letter j   Tall (capital) J J j J j

j j

J j J

© JOHN MURRAY   FROM TALKING TO HANDWRITING

y

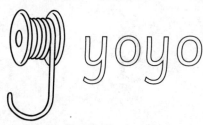 yoyo

y is a tail letter y — top / halfway / bottom y y y y

Letter u and letter y make a practice pattern.

<u>Say and write</u> u changes into u y y

<u>Practice patterns and words</u>

uuyyy

you

yell

yes

Tail letter y   Tall (capital) Y Y y Y y

yy

YyY

g

girl

g is a tail letter g ≡ top / halfway / bottom   g g g g

Letter a and letter g make a practice pattern.

<u>Say and write</u> a changes into agg

Practice patterns and words

ag   ag   gg   gg

go

egg

leg

Tail letter g   Tall (capital) G G g G g

gg

GgG

© JOHN MURRAY · FROM TALKING TO HANDWRITING

qu

qu queen

q is a tail letter q ‾‾ top / halfway / bottom   q q q q

Letter q and letter u always stay together
qu   qu

<u>Say and write</u> q and u make a practice pattern

<u>Practice patterns and words</u>

qu   qu

quiz

quick

quack

Tail letter qu   Tall (capital) Qu Qu

qu qu

Qu qu Qu

p

pipe

Letter p is a tail letter p ——— top ═ halfway bottom   p p p p

Letter p and letter n –pn– make a practice pattern npp

<u>Say and write</u> Letter p, down, up and round pp

<u>Practice patterns and words</u>

pn pn pp

pin

pop

pond

Tail letter p   Tall (capital)P P p P p

pp

PpP

© JOHN MURRAY   FROM TALKING TO HANDWRITING

Letter 'v' shapes
Group 5
Print

v

w

x

z

© JOHN MURRAY   FROM TALKING TO HANDWRITING

V

vase

v is a small halfway letter v ------- top
                                ====== halfway
                                ------ bottom

Letter v is a v shape pattern v v

Copy the picture of

the vase

Practice patterns and words

v v   v   v v

van

vest

very

Small halfway v   Tall (capital) V V v V v

v v v

V v V

© JOHN MURRAY   FROM TALKING TO HANDWRITING

W  worm

w is a small halfway letter w ----- top
----- halfway
----- bottom

Letter w has two (2) v shape patterns w

Say and write Letter v changes into vv
v into w

Copy the picture of

the worm

Practice patterns and words

v w   v w   w w

win

was

week

Small halfway w   Tall (capital) W W w W w

w w

WwW

X

box

x is a small halfway letter x ═══ top
halfway
bottom

Letter x has four (4) v shape patterns ※

Copy the picture of

the box

Practice patterns and words

x x ∨ x x x x

mix

fox

next

Small halfway x   Tall (capital) X X x X x

x x

X x X

© JOHN MURRAY   FROM TALKING TO HANDWRITING

z

z is a small halfway letter z --- top
halfway
bottom

Letter z has two (2) v shape patterns ≥

Copy the picture of

the zip

Practice patterns and words

‾z _z zz

zoo

zebra

zig-zag

Small halfway z   Tall (capital)Z Z z Z z

z z

ZzZ

© JOHN MURRAY   FROM TALKING TO HANDWRITING

3

Handwriting Worksheets – Joining

■ Joining skills - the transition from pencil to pen

Joining letters can begin as soon as children are proficient in letter shape, direction and formation.

There is a diversity of opinion regarding handwriting models used in schools: print, print with entry strokes and exit strokes, print script with no entry strokes but with exit ligatures, joined writing from the start, cursive with many loops and with no loops. It is difficult for a child to change from one learning style to another, thus it is often a case of adapting a model to help children's needs as well as following the handwriting policy of the LEA or the school.

The National Curriculum states: Once pupils can produce a printed style of handwriting fluently they should begin to develop a comfortable joined up style.

The National Curriculum Attainment Target III, Handwriting Requirements stipulates: Pupils should:

Key Stage 1: be taught to develop a comfortable, legible style which follows the conventions of written English, including:

- writing from left to right across the page and from the top to the bottom of the page;
- starting and finishing letters correctly.
- regularity of size and shape of letters;
- regularity of spacing of letters and words.

Key Stage 2: continue to practise the skills acquired during Key Stage 1 and develop legible handwriting in both joined up and printed styles. As pupils become increasingly confident and independent, their handwriting should show greater control and fluency. They should *be taught to use different forms of handwriting for different purposes, eg print for labelling maps or diagrams; a clear, neat hand for finished, presented work; a faster script for notes.*

The requirements of the National Curriculum are followed in the printing and joining sections of this book. Each letter of the alphabet in the print section has an exit ligature to help children when joining letters, the linking of letters with exit strokes and the joining of one letter to another.

A child must be proficient in a cursive joined style of writing with a pencil before an attempt is made to use a pen. Initially many children find the transition from the use of pencil to pen quite difficult. It is often the case that writing with a pen is introduced with little instruction in the use of a new and different writing instrument, therefore specific advice on this point would benefit the child.

One of the main differences between pen and pencil is that there is less friction between the pen and paper with the result that there is a faster 'flow' compared with that of a pencil. This can lead to the pen appearing to 'run away' when writing and this can initially prove daunting. Added to this, mistakes cannot easily be erased, as they can with a pencil, consequently time is needed for confidence to be gained.

The change can be especially difficult for those children who have poor manipulative skills and who find it awkward to control the writing instrument. There may also be some children who lack fine motor control owing to a disability and for whom there is no alternative but the use of pencil. However, these children should also be given the chance to experiment with different writing instruments.

While some schools still favour the use of the modern version of the fountain pen there is a wide range of writing implements available today such as crayons, nylon-tipped pens, fibre tips with various points such as fine and chisel shaped and plastic roller points, etc., but of all these the most commonly used is the ordinary ball point. The essential movements of writing can be taught using any type of writing device.

Children should be encouraged to try out various types of writing implements to get the 'feel' of them before deciding, with the teacher's assistance, which is the most suitable for them in all respects.

Pen shape and style can be left to the choice of the individual but there should be some guidance given by the teacher especially in the matter of size and a comfortable handhold. In the case of a child with a small hand and small fingers a thick-barrelled pen or pencil tends to impede an easy and fluent writing action.

The best way to help children over this transitional period is to anticipate the problems and to supervise constant practice of using pen or pencil with emphasis on joined cursive sequences and of the linking of one letter to another and in the practice of writing individual words initially progressing to a more fluent cursive style in independent work.

◼ Using the worksheets

The joining skills worksheets follow the same five alphabet groups set out in the print section (pp.27 and 28).

- Group 1 c o a u e s
- Group 2 i r n m
- Group 3 l h b k f t d
- Group 4 j y g qu p
- Group 5 v w x z

Each group has an introduction showing the method of joining from the printed form, the formation of each individual letter ligature, exit stroke or joining stroke.

The first worksheets contain instructions which are written primarily for the teacher who is helping the child or children to acquire the writing skills from the printed format. Children may be able to read these sheets for themselves depending upon their individual reading and writing skills which is why they are produced in a juvenile typeface. The teacher will have to use their knowledge of the standard and ability of the child or children concerned. These worksheets give an overview of joining techniques.

The exercises on the remaining sheets should be explained to the children before they copy the worksheets, the teacher choosing the appropriate page and reading the instructions through with the childor children explaining how to follow the exercise, and copy the written words.

In the case of older children who have specific writing difficulties or inconsistencies, an appropriate revision exercise is necessary. Properly orientated letters, letters formed the correct way around should be explained to avoid confusion. Some letters are formed in reverse and it is necessary to indicate the correct movement. The assessment section (p.12) defines such problems which can be explained to the child/children and remedied with practice.

Practice revision

This could take the form of:

- Repeated patterns: Joining letters (p.70) and Practice Patterns (pp.122–126).
- Practice the copying of the initial joining links when progressing from print script to a joined cursive. See Joining letters pp.66–107.
- Specific letter revision using the relevant page for each individual letter for letter practice pp.31–61.
- Practice words for Letter groups 1 and 2. See p.30.

■ Joining skills

Joining

Joining the letters follows the printing sequence of letter groups. The dotted line shows how we join from a simple printed form.

Group 1

c o a u e s   coa ues

Group 2

i r n m   irnm

Group 3

l h b k f t d cd
k f   lhb kft cd

Group 4

j / y / g / qu p   qup

Group 5

v w x z
w x z   vusxz

© JOHN MURRAY   FROM TALKING TO HANDWRITING

<u>Group 1</u>

<u>Letters formed with 'c'</u>

c o a u e s

<u>Joining strokes</u>

c o a u e s

<u>Joined</u>

coa   ues

<u>Group 2</u>

<u>Letters in 'm'</u>

i r n m

<u>Joining strokes</u>

i r n m

<u>Joined</u>

irnm

<u>Group 3</u>

<u>Tall letters – ascenders</u>

l h b k f t d

<u>Joining strokes</u>

l. h. b. k. f. t. d.

<u>Joined</u>

lhb kf td.

hb cd

<u>Group 4</u>

<u>Tail letters – descenders</u>

j y g qu p 3

<u>Joined</u>

qup j y g 3

do not need to join a following letter.

© JOHN MURRAY FROM TALKING TO HANDWRITING

Group 5

<u>Letters formed with `v`</u>

v w x z

x and z change shape to join.

<u>Joining strokes</u>

v˙˙ w˙˙ x˙ z

<u>Joined</u>

vwxz

z changes its shape to a `tail` letter

(descender) for joined writing.

Practice Patterns

cc C cc C

ccc CC ccc

|||-|||-|||-

ℓℓ   ℓℓ

mm   mm

vvv   vvv

uu   uu

ʃⱼ ʃⱼ ʃⱼ

ℓℓ   ℓℓ

|||-|||-|||-

cc C cc C

ccc CC ccc

© JOHN MURRAY   FROM TALKING TO HANDWRITING

Group 1

Letters formed with `c`

c o a u e s

Joining strokes

c o a u e s

Joined

coa   ues

c is a difficult letter to join.

It needs a lot of practice.

c joins at the bottom of each

letter – c c c c ↄ ↄ ↄ ↄ ↄ.

Then it curves back on the

join line and goes into another

c cc cc cc cc C C C C.

Say and write

c curve back into c

Practice

cc cc cc

cCc cCc cCc

ccc CC ccc

© JOHN MURRAY   FROM TALKING TO HANDWRITING

c is a small halfway letter.

c joins from the bottom of the

letter. c· c· c· cc cc cc

Practice

cot

coat

coal

cool

curve

back

race

face

circle

pencil

o joins from the top of the letter o.

<u>Say and write</u>

c into o   co co

<u>Practice</u>

co co co

oa

out

over

only

home

rose

got

won

about

top

© JOHN MURRAY   FROM TALKING TO HANDWRITING

a joins from the curved stand a.

Say and write

c into o into a. a a

Practice

coa coa

aid

ask

all

eat

ate

oat

coat

always

© JOHN MURRAY FROM TALKING TO HANDWRITING

u has a stand & u.

u joins from the bottom of the stand

and curves to join to the next letter.

u. u. u. u u u uu

Practice

uy uy

up

under

tune

sure

fuse

rude

curve

laugh.

© JOHN MURRAY   FROM TALKING TO HANDWRITING

e joins from the bottom curve e· e e.

Practice

ea

eu

eo

eel

eat

seat

seed

these

even

every

seem

s joins from the bottom of the letter.

s. ss ss ss

Practice

si

so

sc

sr

sis

grass

say

was

sister

sun

miss

© JOHN MURRAY   FROM TALKING TO HANDWRITING

Group 2

Letters in 'm'

i r n m

Joining strokes

i r n m

Joined

irnm

i joins from the bottom of the letter ii.

Practice

ie

io

is

sit

ill

list

mile

while

fight

tide

little

© JOHN MURRAY   FROM TALKING TO HANDWRITING

r joins from the top of the letter r...

Say and write

i/i into r

Practice

ir

ri

ra

air

rain

here

hurry

horn

street

marry

from

n joins from the second stand n.

Say and write

i/i into r into n irn n n

Practice

irn irn

in

rain

nice

not

nail

note

runny

nest

send

© JOHN MURRAY   FROM TALKING TO HANDWRITING

m joins from the third stand m m.
123

Say and write

i/i into r into n into m m m

Practice

irnm

main

meat

mole

mud

miss

name

chimney

summer

remember

memory

Group 3

Tall letters – ascenders

l h b k f t d

Joining strokes

l. h. b. k. f. t. d.

Joined

lhb   kf   td.

hb   cd

© JOHN MURRAY   FROM TALKING TO HANDWRITING

Joining letters from the printed

sequence.

Tall letters – ascenders

l h b k f t d
  k f

Say and write

c into d cd cd cd

f and k change shape in joined writing.

f goes down under the line ff

f joins from the bar f--f f

k joins from the bottom of the letter

k- k k

Tall letters usually join from the

bottom l- h- b- k- f-- t- d-d / b

Say and write

c into d to help with reversal difficulties.

Practice

cdcd cdcd

b/d

Say and write

h into b to help with reversal difficulties.

Practice

hb hb

Tall letters are the letters of the alphabet which are taller than all the other letters. They start at the top of the line and finish on the line.

top
on the line

© JOHN MURRAY   FROM TALKING TO HANDWRITING

f f goes down under the line.

t starts just below the top line. t^top _bottom

lhb kf td

d is the only tall letter which

does not start at the top of the

letter — d starts with the letter c,

goes up to the top line and back

down to the bottom line. d

Say and write

c into d

c c·d cd d d

Tall letters

l. h. b. k f t d.

lhb kf td

lhb td

© JOHN MURRAY FROM TALKING TO HANDWRITING

l joins from the bottom of the letter l. l.

ll.

<u>Practice</u>

li   li   li

list

lots

last

sell

tell

silly

like

little

lovely

gladly

© JOHN MURRAY   FROM TALKING TO HANDWRITING

h joins from the last stand of

the letter. h h. hh. h

Practice

hn hn

hit

hat

here

with

white

other

shed

hard

though

b joins from the bottom of the letter.

b travels forward ⟶ b b ⟶ b b.

Start with letter h/h and curve round

into b b b.

Say and write

h/h into b hb hb b

Practice

h b

hb

be

rub

but

butter

baby

because

© JOHN MURRAY   FROM TALKING TO HANDWRITING

k changes its shape to join, k k.

k joins from the bottom k. k.

Practice

kr

ka

ko

ku

knife

keep

track

trick

knight

skid

shake

lake

f changes its shape to join, it goes

down under the line f and joins from

the bar ff fi fo

Practice

fa

fun

of

off

fish

fat

from

traffic

feet

raffle

© JOHN MURRAY   FROM TALKING TO HANDWRITING

t starts just below the top line t.

t joins from the bottom of

the letter t t. tt tt

Practice

to

tot

take

told

what

letter

little

bitter

writing

written.

d is the only tall letter which
does not start at the top of the
letter. Start with letter c, take
your pencil up to the top line and
back down to the bottom line.

top
d, c·d cd d

Say and write

c into d cd d

Practice

cd cd

did

add

does

made

middle

© JOHN MURRAY FROM TALKING TO HANDWRITING

d joins from the bottom of the

letter d.

Say and write

c into d cd cd

Practice

dad

daddy

cod

dab

code

road

candle

read

muddy

<u>Group 4</u>

<u>Tail letters – descenders</u>

j y g qu p 3

<u>Joined</u>

j y g 3 qup

j y g 3 ------- do not need to join

a following letter

© JOHN MURRAY   FROM TALKING TO HANDWRITING

Tail letters — descenders are the letters of the alphabet which are written with the body of the letter on the line and the rest of the letter written below the line.

j y g qu p 3

j y g 3 do not need to join a following letter

Practice patterns

ij ij ij

uy

ag

qu

pn nz

Tail letter j

j does not need to join a following

letter

Say and write

i/i into j   i-j   j

Practice

jug

jet

jump

joy

enjoy

inject

injure

rejoice

eject

© JOHN MURRAY   FROM TALKING TO HANDWRITING

<u>Tail letter</u> y

y does not need to join a following

letter

<u>Say and write</u>

y/y into y   u y   u y

<u>Practice</u>

uy   uy

joy

eye

dye

gym

hymn

type

young

journey

<u>Tail letter g</u>

g does not need to join a following

letter.

<u>Say and write</u>

c into o into a/a into g

<u>c-o-a-g   c-o-a-g   coag</u>

<u>Practice</u>

ag ag

gag

age

cage

gang

night

glove

again

© JOHN MURRAY   FROM TALKING TO HANDWRITING

Tail letter q

q and u stay together qu qu qu.

qu joins from the u stand qu.

Say and write

c into o into a/a into qu

coaqu   coaqu   coaqu

Practice

quick

queen

squeak

equal

square

squeeze

quite

quarter

Tail letter p

p joins from the bottom curve on
the line. p. p. p p pp pp

Practice

pop

put

puppy

open

play

picture

paper

people

please

piece

happy

© JOHN MURRAY   FROM TALKING TO HANDWRITING

Group 5

Letters formed with `v`

v w x z

x and z change shape to join.

Joining strokes

v⁻ w⁻ x⁻ ʒ

Joined

vwxʒ

ʒ changes its shape to a `tail` letter

(descender) for joined writing.

v joins from the top of the letter v⸱⸱

v⸱⸱v   v⸱⸱v

Practice

vi

va

vu

vest

very

valley

save

visit

river

silver

avoid

© JOHN MURRAY   FROM TALKING TO HANDWRITING

w joins from the top of the letter w—w.

wa wi wo wh

Practice

was

well

when

swan

write

twist

away

sweep

swim

flower

town

z changes its shape for joined

writing z ʒ   ʒ is now the same as

a tail letter descender, it does not

need to join a letter that follows it.

z ʒ z ʒ ʒ ʒ

Practice

az

ʒoo

ʒip

ʒigʒag

ʒero

ʒebra

blaze

graze

© JOHN MURRAY   FROM TALKING TO HANDWRITING

x changes its shape when it

joins x x x/x joins from the last

curve x. x. xx xx

Practice

xi

xo

oxo

six

fix

axe

axle

sixty

sixteen.

© JOHN MURRAY   FROM TALKING TO HANDWRITING

4

Perception and Patterning Worksheets

■ Perception and patterning exercises

Sheets 1–11. Verbal exercises teacher/child.

Sheets 12–16. Practice 'patterning' sheets.

A series of simple practical activities have been included to help in the assessment of a child's perceptual understanding and spatial awareness if pupils are showing particular difficulties with letters and using available space. These concepts are discussed in further detail in 'The use of lined paper' : pp4–6.

> Many children are coming into schools lacking in basic perceptual–motor skills. As a result they are less able to participate in the formal educational activities which are organised for them and they are less able to learn from these activities.
>
> *Kephart (1971)*

> It is often the case that some children, after some years of schooling, have been unable to assimilate the intricacies of handwriting and find it difficult to 'see' simple structure and form.
>
> *Frostig and Marlow (1973)*

■ Worksheet 1

1. Show me the <u>top</u> of this page.

2. Show me the <u>bottom</u> of this page.

3. Which is the <u>side</u> of the page?

4. Show me the <u>middle</u> of this page.

<u>Words to learn</u>

top   bottom

side   middle

© JOHN MURRAY   FROM TALKING TO HANDWRITING

■ Worksheet 2

Here is a <u>circle</u>.

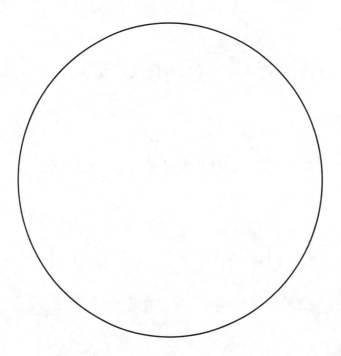

1. Show me the <u>middle</u> of the circle.

2. Show me the <u>top</u> of the circle.

3. Show me the <u>bottom</u> of the circle.

© JOHN MURRAY   FROM TALKING TO HANDWRITING

■ **Worksheet 3**

This is a drawing of a hand.

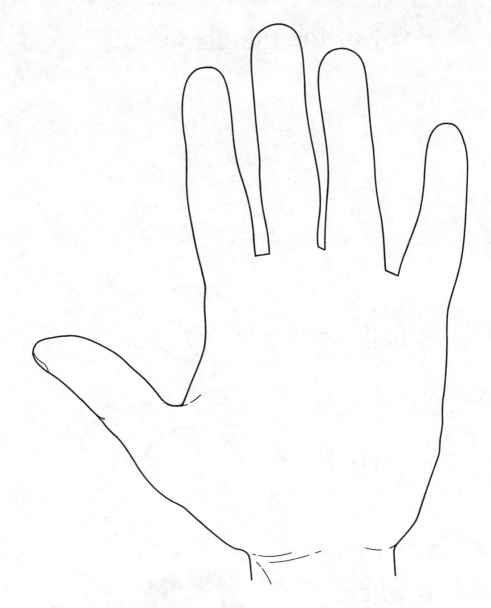

Point to the <u>middle</u> of the hand.

© JOHN MURRAY   FROM TALKING TO HANDWRITING

■ Worksheet 4

<u>Middle</u>

Point to the <u>middle</u> of

a clock

a ball

a circle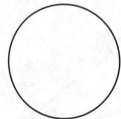

a wheel

© JOHN MURRAY   FROM TALKING TO HANDWRITING

■ Worksheet 5

<u>Middle</u>

Point to the <u>middle</u> of

a square

a shape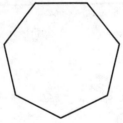

a star

a triangle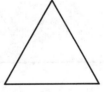

a diamond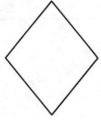

© JOHN MURRAY   FROM TALKING TO HANDWRITING

■ Worksheet 6

Halfway

1. Is this <u>halfway</u> between the <u>top</u> <u>bottom</u> line?

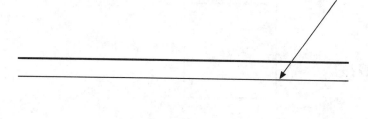

bottom

yes or no?

or

2. Is this <u>halfway</u> between the <u>top</u> and <u>bottom</u> line?

top

bottom

yes or no?

© JOHN MURRAY   FROM TALKING TO HANDWRITING

■ Worksheet 7

Here is a picture.

1. Put a cross <u>below</u> the picture.

2. Put a tick <u>above</u> the picture.

<u>Words to learn</u>

above   below

■ Worksheet 8

Here are two lines.

_____

_____

1. Which is the <u>top</u> line?

Put a cross x on the <u>top</u> line.

2. Draw a line <u>between</u> the two lines.

3. Put a tick ✔ on the <u>bottom</u> line.

© JOHN MURRAY   FROM TALKING TO HANDWRITING

■ Worksheet 9

<u>Across</u>

This line goes <u>across</u> the page.

_____→

These two lines go <u>across</u> the page.

_____→

_____→

Draw some more lines <u>across</u> the page.

*   →

*   →

*   →

© JOHN MURRAY   FROM TALKING TO HANDWRITING

■ Worksheet 10

Can you draw a line <u>across</u> the page <u>halfway</u> between two (2) lines?

top

halfway

bottom

© JOHN MURRAY   FROM TALKING TO HANDWRITING

■ Worksheet 11

Words to learn

long   tall   same

short   small   equal

long   _____

short   _____

tall | | | |
small | | | | | |

same   _____

equal   _____

■ Worksheet 12

Patterns

Practice

C c C c

SS ss SS ss

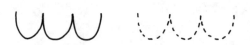

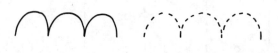

m m m m

||| — ||| --

© JOHN MURRAY   FROM TALKING TO HANDWRITING

■ Worksheet 13

Draw a shape.

Start at the <u>cross</u>.

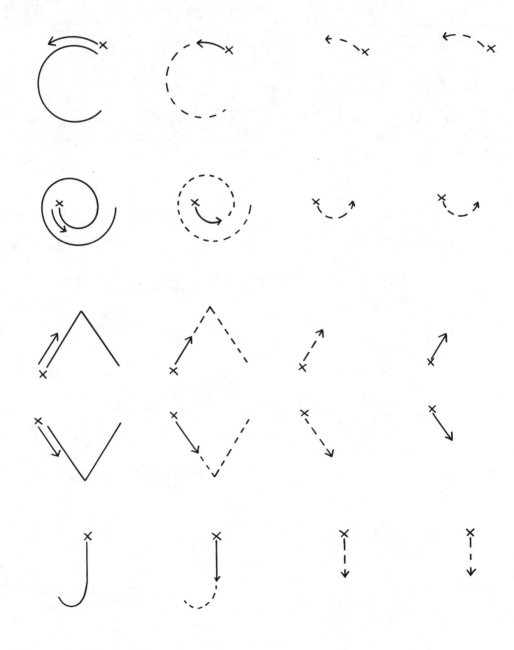

■ Worksheet 14

Curves

Draw a pattern.

Start at the <u>cross</u>.

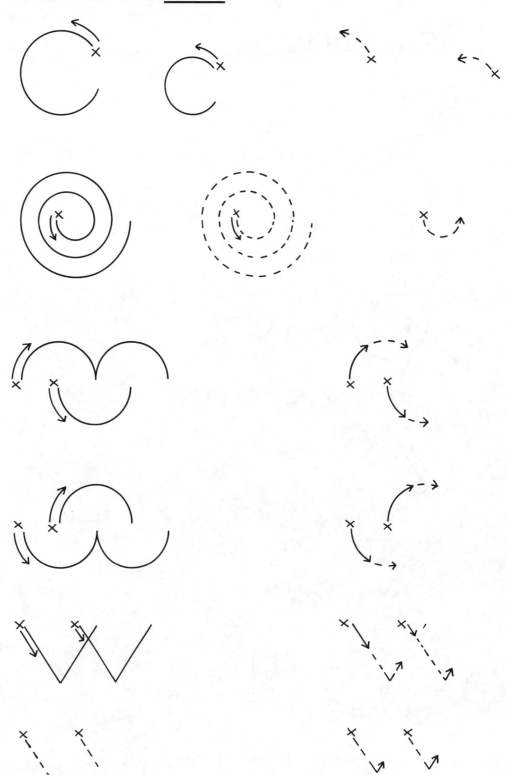

© JOHN MURRAY   FROM TALKING TO HANDWRITING

■ **Worksheet 15**

Circle patterns

A snail

<u>Practice</u>   Start at the <u>cross</u>.

A balloon

<u>Practice</u>   Start at the <u>cross</u>.

© JOHN MURRAY   FROM TALKING TO HANDWRITING

■ Worksheet 16

Draw a pattern.

Start at the <u>cross</u>.

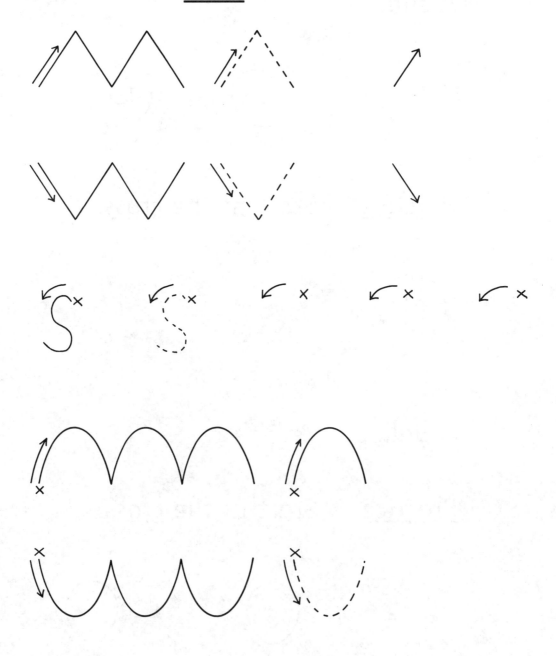

© JOHN MURRAY   FROM TALKING TO HANDWRITING

5
Wallcharts

Note: These wallcharts are a series of sheets to reinforce visually the practical teaching strategies outlined in the book. They can form the basis of classroom wall displays.

Print
Posture

**Is your chair
Too small?**   **Too big?**   **Just right**

**Is your desk/table
Too big?**   **Too small?**   **Just right**

Sit up

**Rest arms on
the desk**

**Feet flat on
the floor**

© JOHN MURRAY   FROM TALKING TO HANDWRITING

Print
Posture – are you sitting properly?

Be wise

Choose a chair the right size

Head up – use your eyes

Feet flat on the floor

Sit up

Arms on the desk

Hands at rest

© JOHN MURRAY   FROM TALKING TO HANDWRITING

Print
Handhold

Hold your pencil/pen the right way, not too near the point, not too tightly, don't press too hard when you write on the paper.

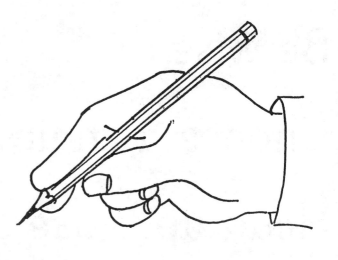

Hold the pencil just above the 'sharpening edge', not too near the pencil point.

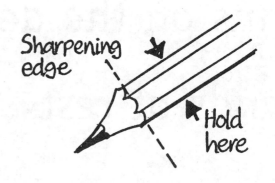

Sharpening edge

Hold here

Hold the pencil with your first finger and thumb just above this line. Rest the pencil on your second finger.

© JOHN MURRAY   FROM TALKING TO HANDWRITING

The alphabet

Each letter has

A letter <u>shape</u>

A letter <u>sound</u>

A letter <u>name</u>

© JOHN MURRAY   FROM TALKING TO HANDWRITING

Letters of the alphabet in no special order

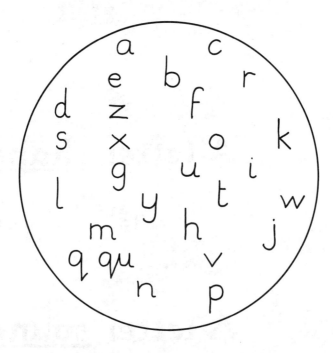

Letters of the alphabet in order

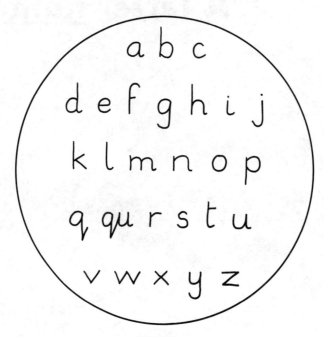

© JOHN MURRAY   FROM TALKING TO HANDWRITING

The alphabet tree

© JOHN MURRAY   FROM TALKING TO HANDWRITING

The capital letters of the alphabet

A   B   C   D

E   F   G   H

I   J   K   L

M   N   O   P

Qu   R   S   T

U   V   W   X

Y   Z

© JOHN MURRAY   FROM TALKING TO HANDWRITING

How can we make the alphabet letters into families so that we can remember them more easily?

Some letters are <u>tall</u>

Some letters are <u>small</u>

Some have <u>tails</u>

Some are '<u>v</u>' shape

We sorted the letters into
five (5) groups

© JOHN MURRAY   FROM TALKING TO HANDWRITING

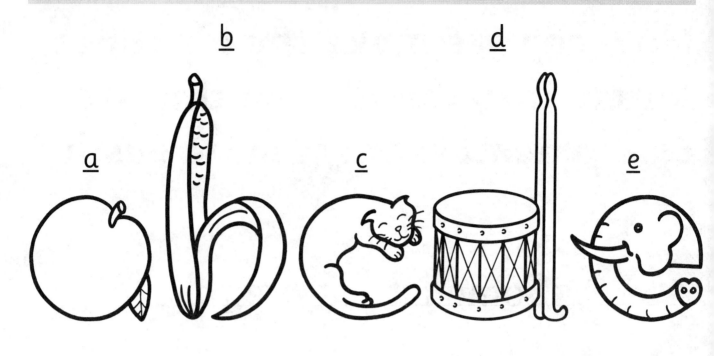

a   b   c   d   e

apple   banana   cat   drum   elephant

- -

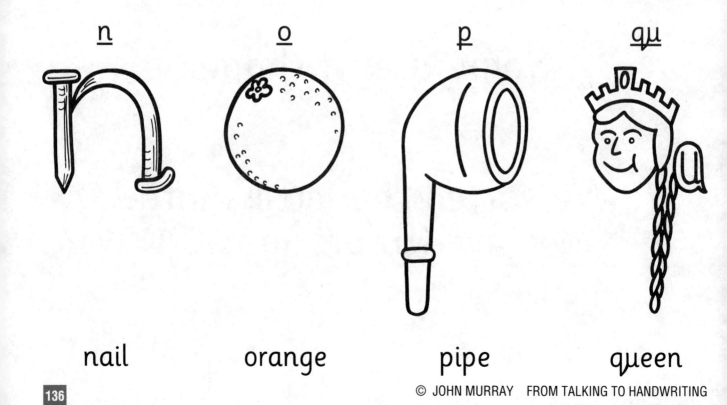

n   o   p   qu

nail   orange   pipe   queen

    © JOHN MURRAY   FROM TALKING TO HANDWRITING

f

g

h

i

fish   girl   horse   indian

t

r   s   u   v

rope   snake   teddy   umbrella   vase

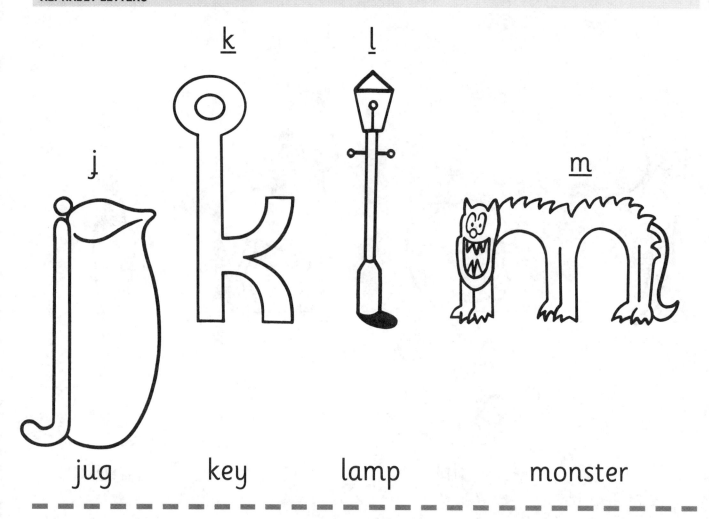

<u>j</u>   <u>k</u>   <u>l</u>   <u>m</u>

jug   key   lamp   monster

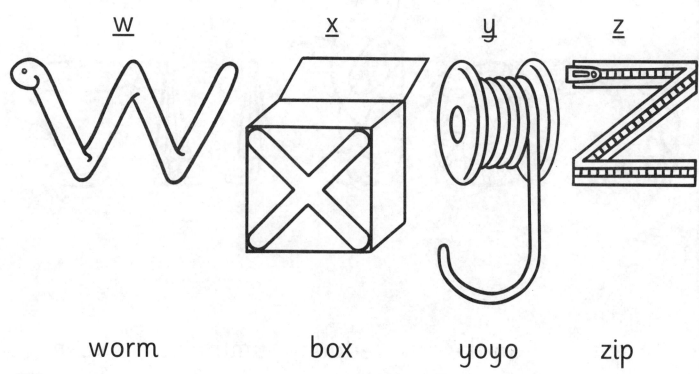

<u>w</u>   <u>x</u>   <u>y</u>   <u>z</u>

worm   box   yoyo   zip

© JOHN MURRAY   FROM TALKING TO HANDWRITING

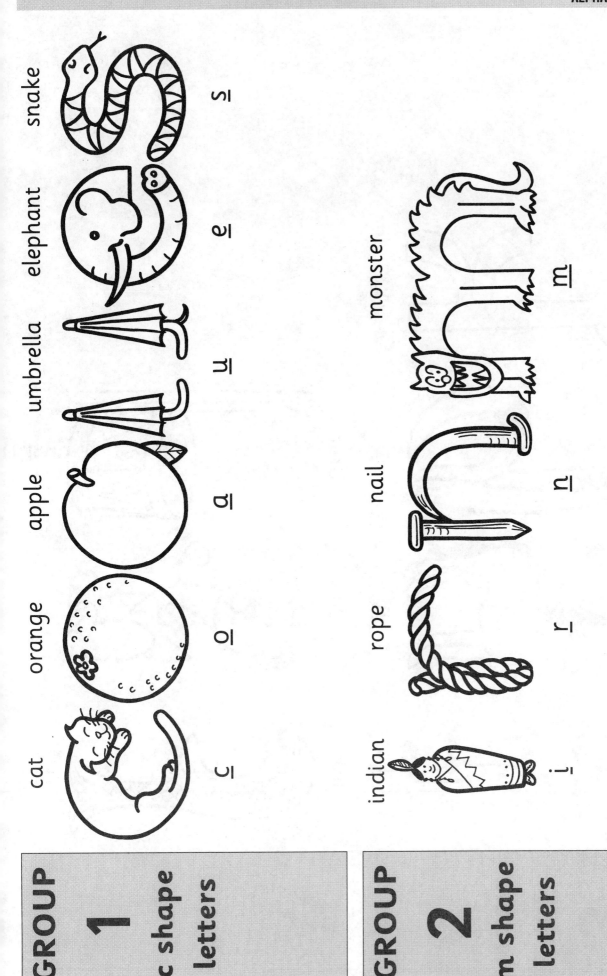

GROUP
1
c shape letters

cat
orange
apple
umbrella
elephant
snake

c
o
a
u
e
s

GROUP
2
m shape letters

indian
rope
nail
monster

i
r
n
m

© JOHN MURRAY   FROM TALKING TO HANDWRITING

GROUP

3

tall
letters

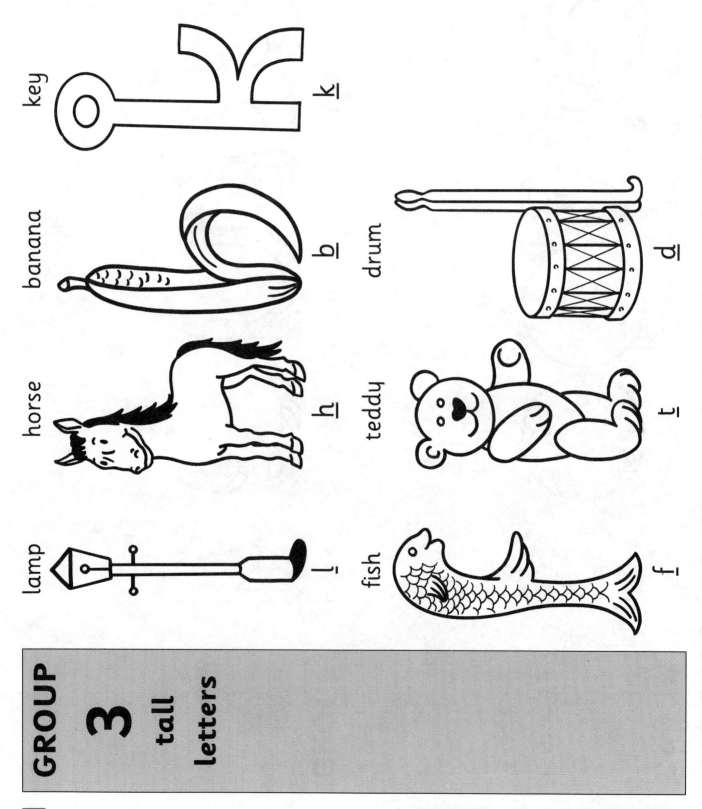

key

k

banana

b

horse

h

lamp

l

drum

d

teddy

t

fish

f

© JOHN MURRAY   FROM TALKING TO HANDWRITING

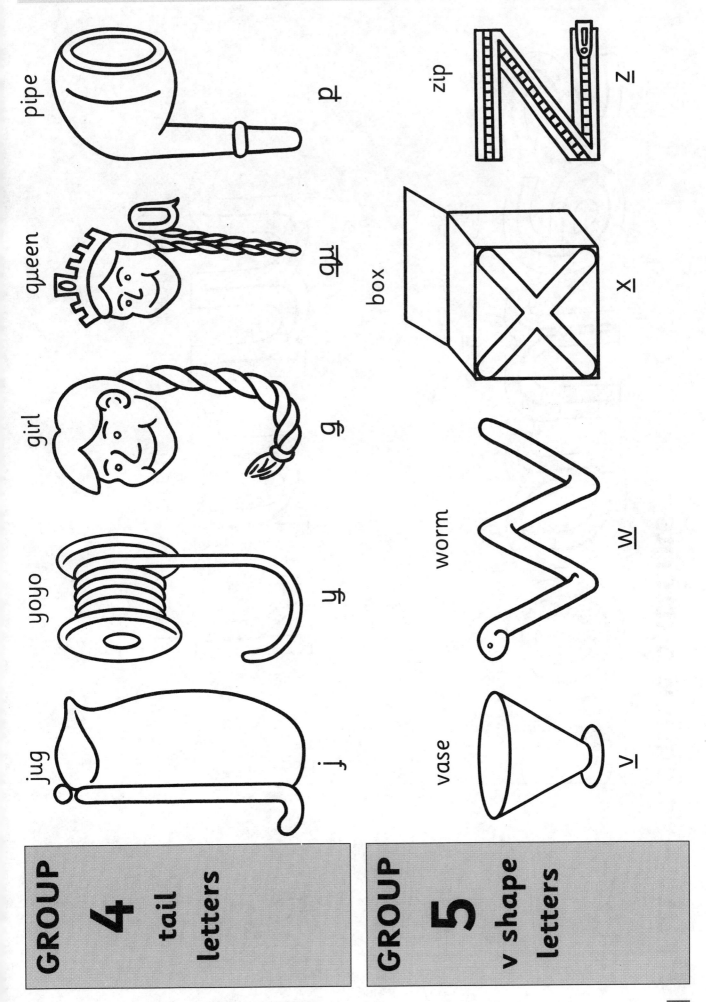

GROUP 4
tail letters

pipe   p

queen   qu

girl   g

yoyo   y

jug   j

GROUP 5
v shape letters

zip   z

box   x

worm   w

vase   v

© JOHN MURRAY   FROM TALKING TO HANDWRITING

Print – Practice patterns

GROUP 1
c shape letters

c
cco
coca
uiu
cee
sss

GROUP 2
m shape letters

i
iirr
iirrn
iirrmim

© JOHN MURRAY   FROM TALKING TO HANDWRITING

GROUP

3

tall

letters

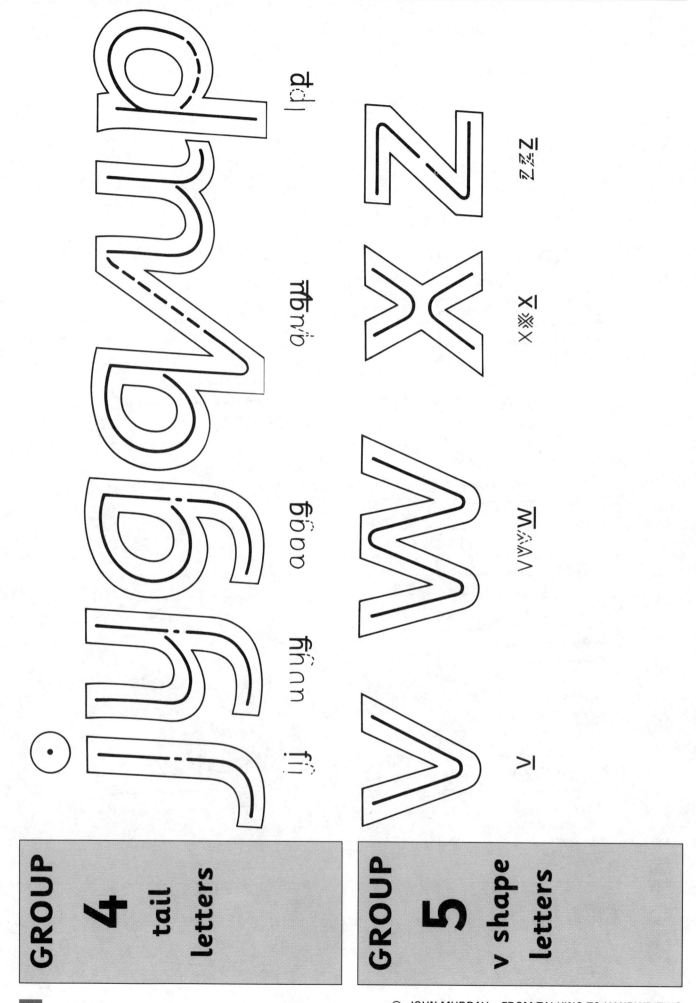

GROUP 4
tail letters

GROUP 5
v shape letters

© JOHN MURRAY   FROM TALKING TO HANDWRITING

144

Points to remember about writing

Rules beginning with the letter <u>Pp</u>

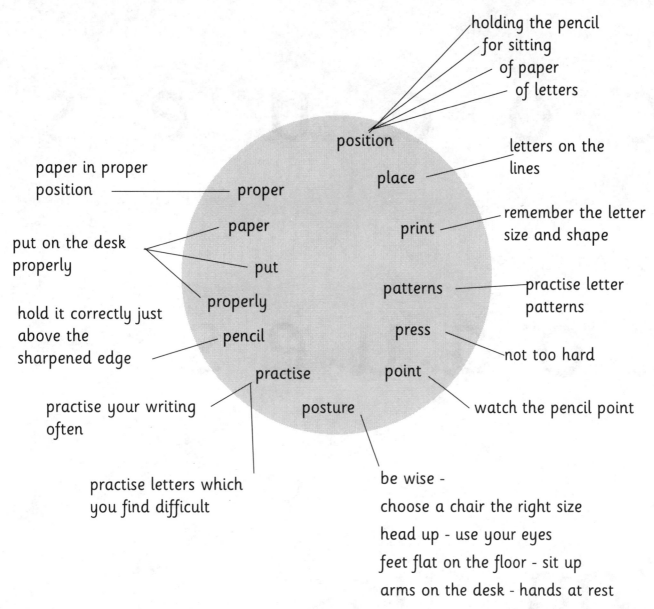

holding the pencil
for sitting
of paper
of letters

position

paper in proper
position — proper

place

letters on the
lines

put on the desk
properly

paper

put

print

remember the letter
size and shape

properly

patterns

practise letter
patterns

hold it correctly just
above the
sharpened edge

pencil

press

not too hard

practise

point

watch the pencil point

practise your writing
often

posture

practise letters which
you find difficult

be wise -

choose a chair the right size

head up - use your eyes

feet flat on the floor - sit up

arms on the desk - hands at rest

persist - keep trying

presentation - neat and tidy
start at the margin

© JOHN MURRAY   FROM TALKING TO HANDWRITING

Joining letters

Group 1
Letter 'c' shapes

Print

c o a u e s

Joining strokes

c. o̤ a. u. e. s.

Joined

coa ues

  © JOHN MURRAY FROM TALKING TO HANDWRITING

Joining letters

Group 2
Letter 'm' shapes

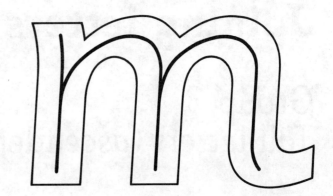

Print

i r n m

Joining strokes

i. r̈ n̈ m̈

Joined

irnm

Joining letters

Group 3
Tall letters (ascenders)

Print

l h b k f t d

Joining strokes

l. h.. b.. k.. f.. t. d..

Joined

lhb kf td

© JOHN MURRAY   FROM TALKING TO HANDWRITING

Joining letters

Group 3
Tall letters (ascenders)

Print

j y g qu p

Joining strokes

j y g

do not need to join
a following letter

join from the base

qu.. p..

For joined writing 'z' changes to 'ʒ' a tail letter
(descender). See Group 5 joining letters on the next
sheet.

© JOHN MURRAY   FROM TALKING TO HANDWRITING

Joining letters

Group 5
Letter 'v' shapes

Print

V W X Z

Joining strokes

V̈ Ẅ Ⅹ. ʒ

Joined

vw∞ʒ

x changes its shape to join – ∞
z changes its shape to join – ʒ
ʒ is now a 'tail' letter (descender) it does not need
to join a following letter – buʒʒ fiʒʒ diʒʒy

   © JOHN MURRAY   FROM TALKING TO HANDWRITING

■ Poems for practice

The following poems are a useful additional medium for handwriting practice. They will also stimulate a child's interest during project work in conjunction with English work and other areas of the Curriculum.

For printing practice

Hurt no living thing   *Christina Rossetti*
To a squirrel   *W B Yeats*
Folk   *Ted Hughes*
A busy day   *Michael Rosen*
Summer song   *E Nesbit*
At the seaside   *R L Stevenson*
Autumn fires   *R L Stevenson*
Please to remember (i)   *Walter de la Mare*
Please to remember (ii)   *Walter de la Mare*
Winter   *Joyce Grenfell*

For joining practice

The postman's here   *Carl Sandburg*
The baby sardine   *Spike Milligan*
Busy day   *Michael Rosen*
Folk   *Ted Hughes*
The pool in the rock   *Walter de la Mare*
Seaside smells   *Dylan Thomas*
Summer song   *E Nesbit*
Autumn fires   *R L Stevenson*
Please to remember (i)   *Walter de la Mare*
Please to remember (ii)   *Walter de la Mare*
Winter   *Joyce Grenfell*

■ Bibliography

Burnhill, P., Hartley, J., Fraser, S., Young, M. (1975) Writing Lines – an Exploratory Study. Programmed Learning and Educational Technology, Vol. 12, No.2.

Fernald, G. (1943). Remedial Techniques in Basic School Subjects. New York: McGraw Hill. Reprint (1989) Leicester. Taskmaster.

Frostig, M., Horne, D., (1964) The Frostig Programme for the Development of Visual Perception. Chicago: Follett Educational Corporation.

Lerner, J. W., (1971) Children with Learning Difficulties. Boston: Houghton Mifflin Co.

Orton, S. T., (1937) Reading, Writing and Speech Problems in Children. New York: Norton.

Paterson, J. (1976) Interpreting Handwriting. London: Macmillan.

Smith, V. H., James, F. E., (1968) Eyes and Education. London: Heinemann.